The Three Little Pigs

This is where a big pig and three
little pigs live.

three pigs

pig

"Little pigs," said the big pig.
"You do not have to live here.
You can live where you like.
You are big now."

"I do not like to do hard things,"
said the first pig.
"I will make a straw house.
The straw I want is here, so
the house will not be hard to make.
I'll make it now."

straw

And he did.

"I do not like to do hard things,"
said the next pig.
"I will make a stick house.
The sticks I want are here, so
the house will not be hard to make.
I'll make it now."

pig

stick

sticks

And he did.

"I want a big brick house,"
said the next pig.
"It will be hard to make.
First, I will have to find bricks.
Then I will have to work and work.
I'll make my house by this big green tree."

And he did.

Then a wolf came to the houses.

First, he came to the straw house.

"Little pig, little pig," said the wolf.

"Can I come in?"

"Not by the hair on my chinny chin chin,"
said the little pig.

"Then I'll huff and I'll puff, and
I'll blow your house in," said the wolf.

And he did.

Next, the wolf came to the stick house.

"Can I come in?" said the wolf.

"Not by the hair on my chinny chin chin,"
said the pig.

"Then I'll huff and I'll puff, and
I'll blow your house in," said the wolf.

And he did.

Then the wolf came to the <u>brick</u> house.

"Can I come in?" said the wolf.

"Not by the hair on my chinny chin chin,"
said the pig.

"Then I'll huff and I'll puff, and
I'll blow your house in," said the wolf.

And he huffed and he puffed.

And he huffed and he puffed.

AND HE HUFFED AND HE PUFFED.

And he did not blow the house in.